Good Grief,

Charlie Brown!

Selected Cartoons from
GOOD GRIEF,
MORE PEANUTS!
VOL. 1

by Charles M. Schulz

A Crest Reprint

CREST
BOOK

Fawcett Publications, Inc., Greenwich, Conn.
Member of American Book Publishers Council, Inc.

Good Grief, Charlie Brown!

KRINKLE

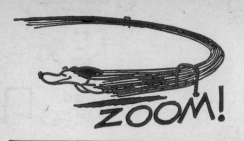

WHEEEEEEEE

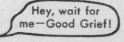